1

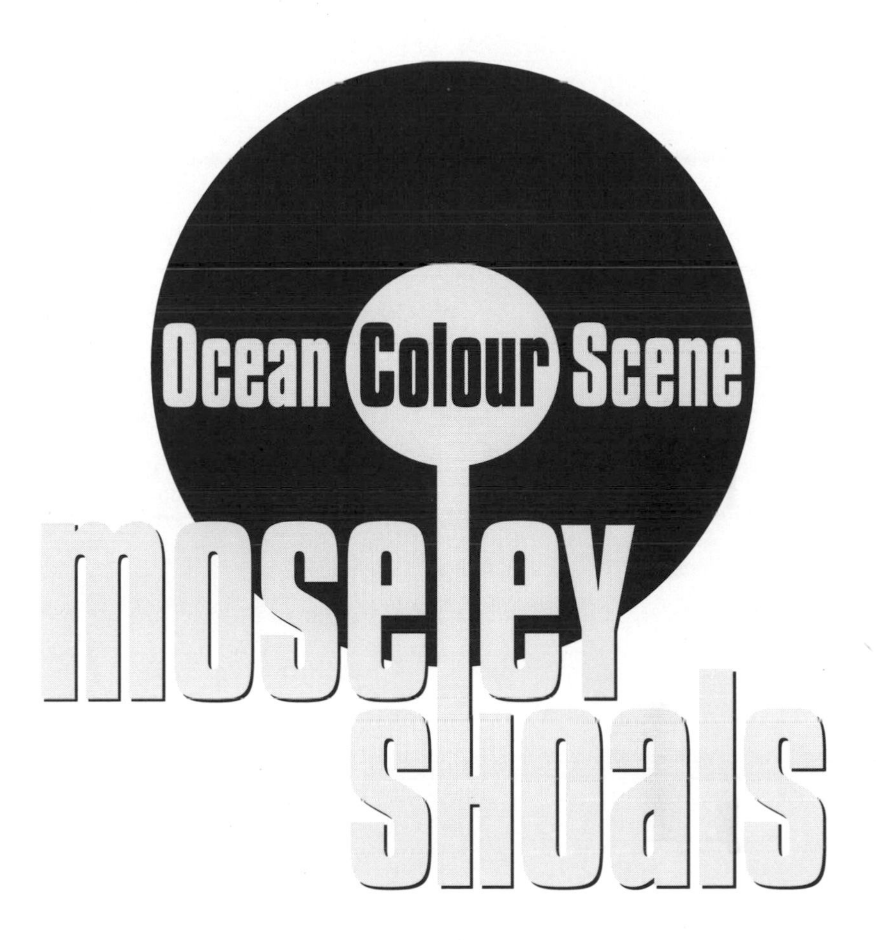

This publication is not authorised for sale in the United States of America and/or Canada

Island Music Limited

£10-95

2

Ocean Colour Scene

moseley shoals

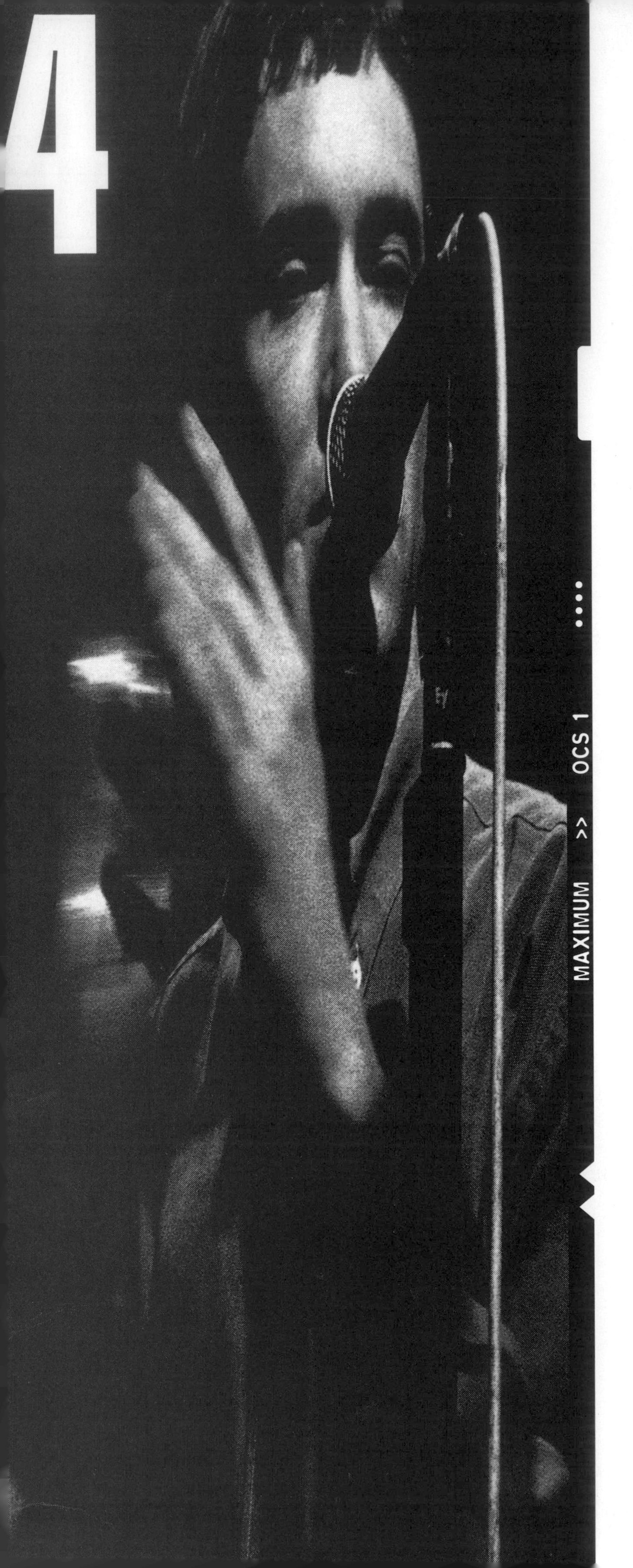

THE RIVERBOAT SONG

I see double up ahead
Where the riverboat swayed beneath the sun
Is where the river runs red
Like a king who stalks the wings and shoots a dove
And frees an eagle instead
It's more or less the same as the things that you said

I see trouble up the road
Like the things you found in love are by the way
And like to cheat on your soul
Like the best and worst of thoughts that lose control
Before you lie on your bed
It's more or less the same as the things that you said

Anyway for all the things you know
tell me why does the river not flow
Anyway for all the things you said
why does the river run red
Anyway for all the things you've seen
tell me when will the river run green
And anyway for all the things you know
tell me why does the river not flow

It's more or less the things
you fail to say in your way that's your trouble
Like a king who stalks the wings
and shoots the moon and the stars
And his double
It's more or less the same as the things that you said

I see double up ahead
Where the riverboat swayed beneath the sun
Is where the river runs red
I see double - that's my trouble

THE DAY WE CAUGHT THE TRAIN

I never saw it as the start it's more a change of heart
Rapping on the windows, whistling down the chimney pot
blowing off the dust in the room
where I forgot I laid my plans in solid rock
Stepping through the door
like a troubadour whiling just an hour away,
looking at the trees on the roadside feeling it's a holiday

You and I should ride the coast
and wind up in our favourite coats just miles away.
Roll a number write another song
like Jimmy heard the day he caught the train.

He sipped another rum and coke and told a dirty joke
Walking like Groucho sucking on a number 10
Rolling on the floor with the cigarette burns walked in
I'll miss the crush and I'm home again
Stepping through the door
with the night in store whiling just an hour away,
step into the sky in the star bright feeling its brighter day.

You and I should ride the tracks
and find ourselves just wading through tomorrow
and you and I when we're coming down
we're only getting back
and you know I feel no sorrow.

When you find that things are getting wild
don't you need days like these.

THE CIRCLE

Saturday afternoon
the sunshine pours like wine
through your window
But I know golden June
can turn an empty grey
against your window
And I feel like
I'm on the outside of a circle

If I walk by the trees
I'll catch the falling leaves
if the wind blows
But I know all this means
is whiling on the hours
watching side shows

Will I turn my coat to the rain
I don't know
But I'm going somewhere
I can warm my bones

Fare you well I'll carry me away
and sing for those I know
upon their birthdays.

LINING YOUR POCKETS

Well hello my old friend
you know I've been away
I'm not asking for much
but please remember my name

You've been lining your pockets
for no other reason
Than to buy up the things
that I gave without reasonable pay
Well I wondered through fortune
and I flirted with fame
but we never got the money
we always gave it away

Old benchmark on the park
he got lost on the world
but he doesn't seem
to know about any of it at all
he said - all the things that I wanted
you know I had to pay and pay....
and so I say

FLEETING MIND

The brilliance of my fleeting mind
Chimes like voices in foreign caves
it chimes in time - takes me where I'm going

Alone my fleeting mind is knowing
believe it when I pin it down

And that's not hard to forget
with my hands upon my knees
You will steal from my fleeting mind

Remember all our words
they are just smoke rings in the rain:
that's just a poem in brilliant places
but poets, they are too grim
they steal like party thieves
from crowded rooms
to rhyme their homes with better places

The brilliance of their minds
will seek with never knowing
alone my fleeting mind is knowing
believe it when I pin it down

And that's not hard to forget
with my thought like sitting leaves
I believe in my fleeting mind.

40 PAST MIDNIGHT

When I'm waiting standing on the corner
And it's coming 40 past the hour
In the midnight lonely freezing hour
With my insides churning in the gutter

And I'm waiting 40 past midnight
Catching rain the soda light
Won't you come & call me to your window
Please don't leave me waiting on the corner

We could have the best time
if you lighten up your life

With my pockets holey in the inside
With my bus ride rolling in the gutter
But if you would only light your lamp light
Then I would be here than any other

Well I'm waiting 40 past midnight
Catching cold in the pouring rain
Won't you come & take me to your door
So I can take myself home again

When I'm waiting standing on the corner
And the soda light begins to flicker
And it's getting 40 past the hour
And I think I won't see what I figure

Well I'm waiting freezing on the inside
Staring up at your window pane
If you won't come see me this evening
I can see myself here again

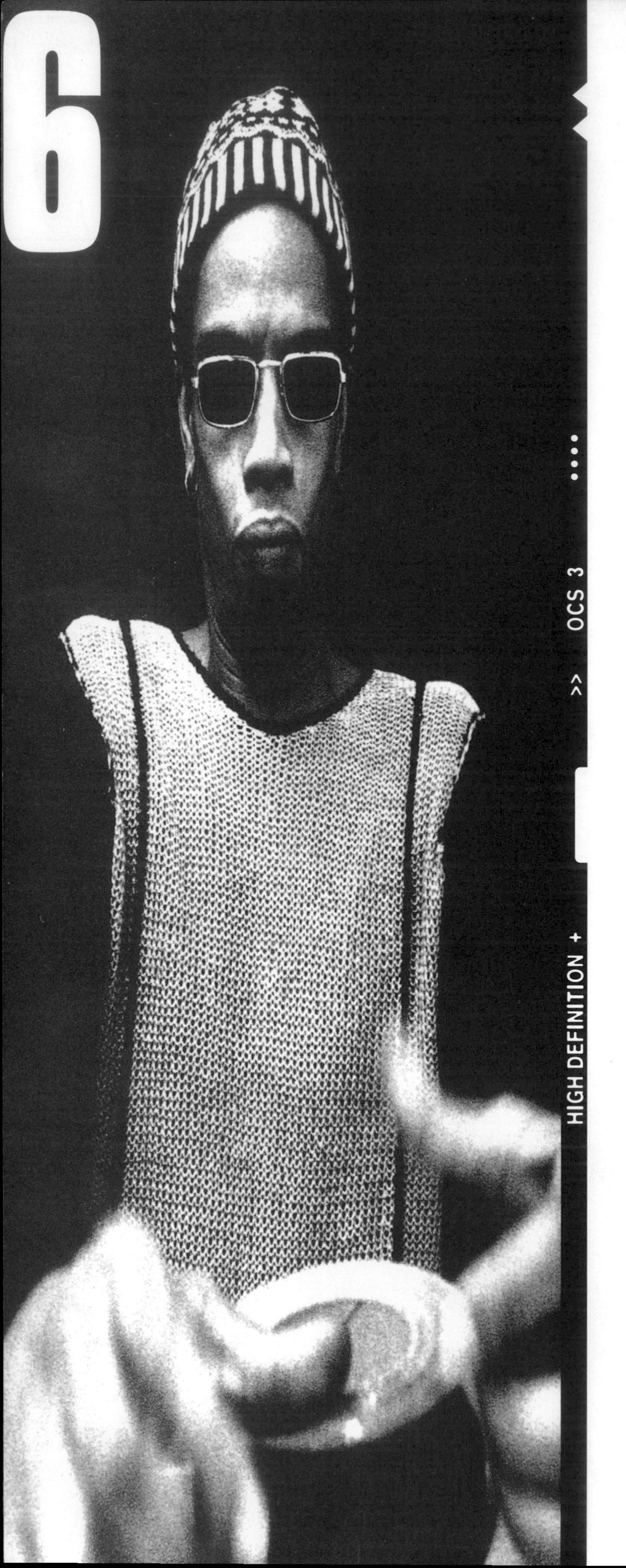

ONE FOR THE ROAD

No I never knew you
We both went to different schools

Me so sacred of the rules
You chasing all the girls
Now it seems to me
We never grew up
we just got ourselves free
Inventing what we could be
To buy all their curls

Get up and dance - Get up and smile
Get up and drink to the days
that who are gone in the shortest while

Get up and dance - Get up and smile
Get up and drink to the ones
who are gone in the shortest while

She was just eighteen she collapsed
and they took her away
She didn't make it for more than an hour
Then she was gone
What do you say
when someone's been taken away
that way
before they've had a day
to fly in the sun.

IT'S MY SHADOW

Who is that upon the stairs
acting like he don't know where
and who is laying down all the cards
and giving me the wrong things to say
and like a wheel on the table
He's a Cain to my Abel:
Oh.....it's my shadow
Paralysed until the sun lights the daytime
as she comes into my day
It's my shadow......a confessor to my dreams
casting ribbon round my feet......Oh into my day

Happy in the time when I would have been there to see you
Happy in the time when I would have been there at all
Happy when the night is gone and I believe you
Happy when the night is gone and I need a call.

Who is chasing in the wind all the letters never sent
and who is dusting down the stairs
and giving me the wrong moves to make.
And like a wheel on the table, he's a Cain to my Abel
dancing upon the floor, it's my shadow
making eyes until the sun blinds the daytime
as she comes into my day
It's my shadow like a willow to my stream
casting heaven round my feet
Oh......into my day

When you find that things are getting wild is that
the hardest smile that you can ever feel.

And if my shadow comes a creeping
Then I'll always find me sleeping in the sun.

POLICEMEN & PIRATES

The house caught on fire in the winter
the bosses lay slain
and each of the workers decided to ten-fold their pay
and they saw in the mirror
the sun had been shot down in flames
and nobody minded the hole in the sky or the rain

but it doesn't really matter
when the judgements are said
'cos we all take our chances to find out
romance is in some others bed
and you might burn your fingers
hook your best rings for those
who'd have you standing naked
the publicity auction the use of a hose

all the children were laughing
their faces in half at the pain
of the girl who loved talking to walls
and jumping at trains
and the words that ring true
in the playground of fools will remain
and nobody minded the hole in the sky
or the rain

but it doesn't really matter
when the lights have been read
'cos we all take our chances to glance
at the wife in the opposite bed
and I bet Nero and Pilate could easily explain
how policemen & pirates get stoned in glass housed
just finding their way.

THE DOWNSTREAM

Lay down your head & look to your window
Where do you go when it's not where you're going
And how do you see when the light isn't shining
Where you could be if you worked out the timing

And how does it feel
when each word comes back so real & true
And how do you do the things you do to you

If I were a king & you were a lady
What would I sing to say what I'm saying
And would you believe the verses left open
My heart on my sleeve the rhyming all broken

And how does it feel
when each word comes on so real & true
And how do you do the things you do to you

Sell me a river and I'll skate away
to the downstream where I did play
So easy minded like a hill on the skyline
tripped up and blinded getting lost on the sidelines

And how does it feel
when each world comes on so real & true
And how do you do the things you do to you

YOU'VE GOT IT BAD

And if I could hold you
where would you belong
Sitting here to reason
how the world's gone wrong
And if I could listen
to half the words you say
Would your pathway glisten
and help you on your way

Oh you've got it bad
But you shouldn't expect any cover
Oh you've got it so bad
Worse than any other

If I was in your shoes
would it be the same
Would you sit in silence
while I dish out the blame
And if the world was laughing
would you close your ears
There is no creed of chanting
to make the world more clear

If I bought you flowers
would you watch them grow
Spring time is for certain
to follow on the snow

GET AWAY

Well I used to be a listener -
there was nothing left to get
About what you are
and what you haven't been yet
and some of them like to tell a story that is long
and old and couch it in indifference and the wine
that they were sold to get away

Well someone's got to tell them
that it's not deserved,
rehearsed or written down
by playwrights over time
just picking up on the nerve.
And some of them got a difference
that they reserve for you
Well I like them all but I don't trust any of them
well shouldn't you, just get away

Well I used to think
my freedom was a lot of things I'd give,
demanding on my time
but I had so much time to give,
and I used to think
that everything was a knee in what you are.
But finding the truth
that hurts, so I never went for that,
I always bet away

Well it comes down to the fact
that I'm now different from the past,
demanding all my ideals it's just trying to make them last,
and some of the things that you say
they're ringing home so true.
I hang my head out of the door and I follow you,
yes I follow you and get away

101% >> OCS 4

THE RIVERBOAT SONG

Words & Music by Simon Fowler, Steve Cradock, Oscar Harrison & Damon Minchella.

© Copyright 1995 Island Music Limited, 47 British Grove, London W4.
All Rights Reserved. International Copyright Secured.

Bm7
(3º instrumental)
dou- ble up a - head,
(Verses 2, 3 & 4 see block lyric)
(3º vocal)
Em7
where the riv - er - boat sways be- neath the sun is where the ri - ver runs
To Coda
Bm7
Em7
red. Like a king who stalks the wings and shoots a
Bm7
dove and frees an ea - gle in - stead. It's

F♯
G
A
more or less the same as the things that you said.
1.
Bm
2. I see
2, 3.
♩. = 78
Bm7
D
E
A
And a-ny-way for all the things you know, tell me why does the riv-er not
Bm
D
E
A
flow? And a-ny-way for all the things you said, tell me why does the riv-er run

Bm
D
E
A
red? And a-ny-way for all the things you've seen, tell me when will the riv-er run
Bm
D/A
E/G♯
fr2
green? And a-ny-way for all the things you know, tell me why does the riv-er not
Bm
3º
Bm7
flow?
D.%. al Coda
(after 3º ending)
Coda
F♯m7
dou-ble, that's my

Verse 2:
I see trouble up the road,
Like the things you found in love are by the way
And like to cheat on your soul.
Like the best and worst of thoughts that lose control
Before you lie on your bed.
It's more or less the same as the things that you said.

Verse 3:
Instrumental 4 bars
It's more or less the things you fail to say in your way.
That's your trouble,
Like a king who stalks the wings
And shoots the moon and the stars and his double.
It's more or less the same as the things that you said.

*Verse 4 (**D.%.**):*
I see double up ahead,
Where the riverboat swayed beneath the sun
Is where the river runs red.
I see double, that's my trouble.

THE DAY WE CAUGHT THE TRAIN

Words & Music by Simon Fowler, Steve Cradock, Oscar Harrison & Damon Minchella.

© Copyright 1995 Island Music Limited, 47 British Grove, London W4.
All Rights Reserved. International Copyright Secured.

D
C
B
I laid my plans in so - lid rock.
Em
A
Step- ping through the door like a trou - ba- dour, whil- ing just an hour a - way,
Em
A
look- ing at the trees on the road - side, feel- ing it's a ho - li - day.
D
A♯dim
Bm
A/C♯
You and I should ride the coast and wind up in our fav - 'rite coats just

Em
G
miles a - way.
Roll a num - ber,
A
write an - oth - er song like Jim - my heard the day he caught thc train.
D
A
G
Em
Oh la la, oh la la.
D
A
G
Em
1.
Oh la la, oh la.

2.
A
You and I should ride the tracks and find ourselves just wad-
D
A
-ing through to-mor-row.
And you and I when we're
com-ing down, we're on-ly get-ting back and you know I feel no sor-
D
(Vocal tacet 1º)
A
G
Em
-row. Oh la la, oh la la.

Verse 2:
He sipped another rum and Coke and told a dirty joke.
Walking like Groucho, sucking on a number 10.
Rolling on the floor with the cigarette burns walked in
I'll miss the crush and I'm home again.
Stepping through the door
With the night in store, whiling just an hour away.
Step into the sky in the star bright feeling it's a brighter day.

THE CIRCLE

Words & Music by Simon Fowler, Steve Cradock, Oscar Harrison & Damon Minchella.

© Copyright 1995 Island Music Limited, 47 British Grove, London W4.
All Rights Reserved. International Copyright Secured.

D
A
Bm
G
(Verse 3 see block lyric)
gol - den June can turn an emp - ty grey
'gainst your win - dow.
/G
/F♯
/E
(𝄋. only)
and I (won't)
To Coda
G
C/G
A
D/A
feel like I'm on the out - side of
1.
F♯m/C♯
a cir - cle.
2. If I walk
3

2.
D
C
G
a cir - cle.
Will I turn my coat to the
rain?
I don't know,
but I'm go - ing some -
- where I can warm my bones.
D.%. al Coda
3. Fare you well
Coda
A
C/G
I won't feel like
I'm on the

Verse 2:
If I walk by the trees
I'll catch the falling leaves
If the wind blows.
But I know all this means
Is whiling on the hours
Watching side-shows.

Verse 3 (**D.%.**)*:*
Fare you well, I'll carry me away
And sing for those I know
Upon their birthdays.

LINING YOUR POCKETS

Words & Music by Simon Fowler, Steve Cradock, Oscar Harrison & Damon Minchella.

© Copyright 1995 Island Music Limited, 47 British Grove, London W4.
All Rights Reserved. International Copyright Secured.

To Coda
C
/B
/A
/G
F
B♭/F
F
I'm not ask-ing for much but please re-mem-ber my name.
'Cause you've been
lin-ing your pock-ets for no oth-er rea-son than to buy up the things that I gavc with-out rea-son-a-ble
1.
2.
pay.
pay.
D.%. al Coda

Verse 2:
Well I wondered through fortune
And I flirted with fame.
But we never got the money,
We always gave it away.

Verse 3:
Old benchmark on the park,
He got lost on the world.
But he doesn't seem to know
About any of it at all.

40 PAST MIDNIGHT

Words & Music by Simon Fowler, Steve Cradock, Oscar Harrison & Damon Minchella.

© Copyright 1995 Island Music Limited, 47 British Grove, London W4.
All Rights Reserved. International Copyright Secured.

G7
with my in - sides churn - ing in the gut - ter. And I'm wait - ing for -
- ty past mid - night, catch - ing rain in the so - da light, _
D7
won't you come and call _ me to your win - dow? Please don't leave me wait -
A
- ing on the cor - ner. We could have the best _ time if you

To Coda
1.
Bm
G
D7
light - en up your life.
2.
E♭5
Play 3 times

D7
D.%. al Coda
Play 4 times
Coda
A
Bm
G
We could have the best time if you light - en up your life.
D7♭9
fr4

Verse 2:
With my pockets holey in the inside,
With my bus ride rolling in the gutter,
But if you would only light your lamp light,
Then I would be here than any other.

Well I'm waiting 40 past midnight,
Catching cold in the pouring rain.
Won't you come and take me to your door,
So I can take myself home again?

We could have the best time
If you lighten up your life.

Verse 3:
When I'm waiting, standing on the corner,
And the soda light begins to flicker,
And it's getting 40 past the hour,
And I think I won't see what I figure.

Well I'm waiting, freezing on the inside,
Staring up at your window pane,
If you won't come see me this evening
I can see myself here again.

We could have the best days
If you lighten up your life.

to Coda

FLEETING MIND

Words & Music by Simon Fowler, Steve Cradock, Oscar Harrison & Damon Minchella.

© Copyright 1995 Island Music Limited, 47 British Grove, London W4.
All Rights Reserved. International Copyright Secured.

E
D
time, takes me where I'm go-ing. A-lone my
(Verses 2 & 3 see block lyric)
Cmaj7
B7
fleet-ing mind is know-ing, be-lieve it when I pin it
E
D
To Coda
A
down. And that's not hard
E
D
to for-get, with my hands up-on my knees,

1.
A
E
you will steal from my fleeting mind.
E
Dmaj7
Re-mem-ber all our words they are just smoke rings in the rain: that's just a
Cmaj7
B7
po - em in bril - liant pla - ces. But
E
F♯m
po-ets, they are too grim, they steal like par-ty thieves from crowd-ed rooms to rhyme their homes

Cmaj7
B7
with bet- ter pla - ces.
2. The bril - liance of their
2.
Em
mind.
Em
Asus4
Em

Asus4
Em
B7
D.%. al Coda
3. The bril - liance of their
Coda
A
E
hard to for - get,
D
A
E
D
and that's not hard to for - get,
and that's not
A
E
hard to for - get,

Verse 2:
The brilliance of their minds
Will seek with never knowing.
Alone my fleeting mind is knowing,
Believe it when I pin it down.

And that's not hard to forget,
With my thoughts like sifting leaves
I believe in my fleeting mind.

Verse 3:
The brilliance of their minds
Seeks with never knowing.
Alone my fleeting mind is showing,
Believe it when I pin it down.

ONE FOR THE ROAD

Words & Music by Simon Fowler, Steve Cradock, Oscar Harrison & Damon Minchella.

© Copyright 1995 Island Music Limited, 47 British Grove, London W4.
All Rights Reserved. International Copyright Secured.

C
G
F
3
we nev - er grew up, we just got ourselves free,
in-vent-ing what we could be
C
D
to buy all their curls.
Get up and dance,
C
G
C
G
get up and smile,
get up and drink
F
C
D
1.
to the days that are gone in the short-est while.

2, 3.
C
G
Get up and dance, get up and smile,
C
G
F
get up and drink to the ones who are gone
C
D
in the short - est while. I sing my sor -
G
D
G
- row, I sing my sor - row,

Verse 2:
She was just eighteen,
She collapsed and they took her away.
She didn't make it for more than an hour,
Then she was gone.
What do you say
When someone's been taken away
Before they've had a day
To fly in the sun?

Verse 3:
No I never knew knew you,
We both landed up as different fools,
Me so scared of the rules,
You chasing all the girls.
Now it seems to me,
We never grew up, we just got ourselves free,
Inventing what we could be
To buy all their curls.

IT'S MY SHADOW

Words & Music by Simon Fowler, Steve Cradock, Oscar Harrison & Damon Minchella.

© Copyright 1995 Island Music Limited, 47 British Grove, London W4.
All Rights Reserved. International Copyright Secured.

C
F
it's my shadow, a confessor to my
Gm
B♭
C
F
C
dreams, casting ribbons round my feet oh into my day. It's my
F
Gm
shadow, making eyes until the sun lights the daytime as she
B♭
C
F
comes, oh, into my day.
fr3

E♭
B♭
F
Hap - py in the time when I would have been there to see you.
E♭
B♭
F
Hap - py in the time when I would have been there at all.
Gm
D7/F♯
Gm
Hap - py when the night is gone and I be - lieve you.
A7
Bm
G
Hap - py when the night is gone and I need a call.

D A Bm G D A
I need a call.
Bm G D F#7 Bm G D A
D G
Who is chas-ing in the wind all the let-ters nev-er
Am C D G D/F#
sent? Who is dust-ing down the stars and giv-ing me the

Em
Am
C
wrong moves to make, and like a wheel on the ta - ble, he's a Cain to my A - bel.
D
G
Danc-ing up-on the floor, it's my sha-dow, mak-ing eyes un-til the
Am
C
D
G
D
sun blinds the day-time as she comes, oh, in - to my day. It's my
G
Am
sha-dow, like a wil-low to my stream, cast - ing hea - ven round my

C
D
G
feet, oh, in - to my day.
D
Am
D
When you find that things are get-ting wild is that the hard-est smile that you can ev - er feel?
G
D
Am
D
When you find that things are get-ting wild is that the hard-est smile that you can ev - er feel?
G
Pa - ra - lysed un - til the

Am
C
G
C
G
sun lights the day - time as she comes.
And if my
Am
D
Am
D
sha - dow comes a' - creep - ing then I know I'll find me sleep - ing in the
G
Am
D
Am
D
sun.
G
D
Am
D
Repeat to fade
When you find that things are get-ting wild is that the hard-est smile that you can ev - er feel?

POLICEMEN & PIRATES

Words & Music by Simon Fowler, Steve Cradock, Oscar Harrison & Damon Minchella.

© Copyright 1995 Island Music Limited, 47 British Grove, London W4.
All Rights Reserved. International Copyright Secured.

A
D
A
E
D
of the work - ers de - ci - ded to ten - fold their pay. And they saw
in the mir - ror the sun had been shot down in flames, and no -
- bo - dy mind - ed the hole in the sky or the rain.
But it does - n't real - ly mat - ter when the judge - ments are

A
E
said 'cause we all take our chan - ces to find out ro - mance
D
A
is in some - oth - er's bed.
And you might burn your
E
D
A
fin - gers, hock your best rings for those
E
D
who'd have you stand - ing na - ked, then pub - lic - ly auc - tion the use of a hose.

To Coda
1.
2.
A
E
2. All the child -
B♭
F
Edim
D
B♭
F
E
D
3.
D.%. al Coda
3. The house -
And it does - n't real - ly mat -

Verse 2:
All the children were laughing
Their faces in half at the pain
Of the girl who loved talking to walls
And jumping at trains.
And the words that ring cruel
In the playground of fools will remain,
And nobody minded the hole in the sky
Or the rain.

But it doesn't really matter
When the rights have been read
'Cause we all take our chances to glance
At the wife in the opposite bed.
And I bet Nero and Pilate
Could easily explain
How policemen and pirates get stoned in glass houses
Just finding their way.

D.%.
And it doesn't really matter
When the rights have been read
'Cause we all take our chances to glance
At the wife in the opposite bed.
And I bet Nero and Pilate
Could easily explain
How policemen and pirates get stoned in glass houses
Just finding their way.

YOU'VE GOT IT BAD

Words & Music by Simon Fowler, Steve Cradock, Oscar Harrison & Damon Minchella.

© Copyright 1995 Island Music Limited, 47 British Grove, London W4.
All Rights Reserved. International Copyright Secured.

E♭
fr6
F
- son how the world's gone wrong.
And if I could lis -
- ten to half the words you say,
would your path - way glis - ten and help you on your way?
Oh you've got it bad, but you

F
never should ex - pect cov - er. Oh you've got it so
Eb
fr6
bad, worse than an - y oth - er.
F
Eb
fr6
To Coda 𝄌 1.
2.
F sus4
F
Eb sus4
Eb

Verse 2:
If I was in your shoes
Would it be the same?
Would you sit in silence
While I dish out the blame?
And if the world was laughing
Would you close your ears?
There is no creed of chanting
To make the world more clear.

Verse 3:
If I bought you flowers
Would you watch them grow?
Spring time is for certain
To follow on the snow.
But if I could hold you
Where would you belong?
Sitting here to reason
How the world's gone wrong.

THE DOWNSTREAM

Words & Music by Simon Fowler, Steve Cradock, Oscar Harrison & Damon Minchella.

© Copyright 1995 Island Music Limited, 47 British Grove, London W4.
All Rights Reserved. International Copyright Secured.

G
D
Am
C
where you could be
if you worked out the tim - ing?
And
C
G
D
how does it
feel when the word comes on
so
real
and
true?
And
To Coda
Am
C
G
D
Am
G
D
how
do you do the things you do to you?
3
3:2
D.%. al Coda
Am
C
D
G
D
Am
C
D
3
3
3:2
3

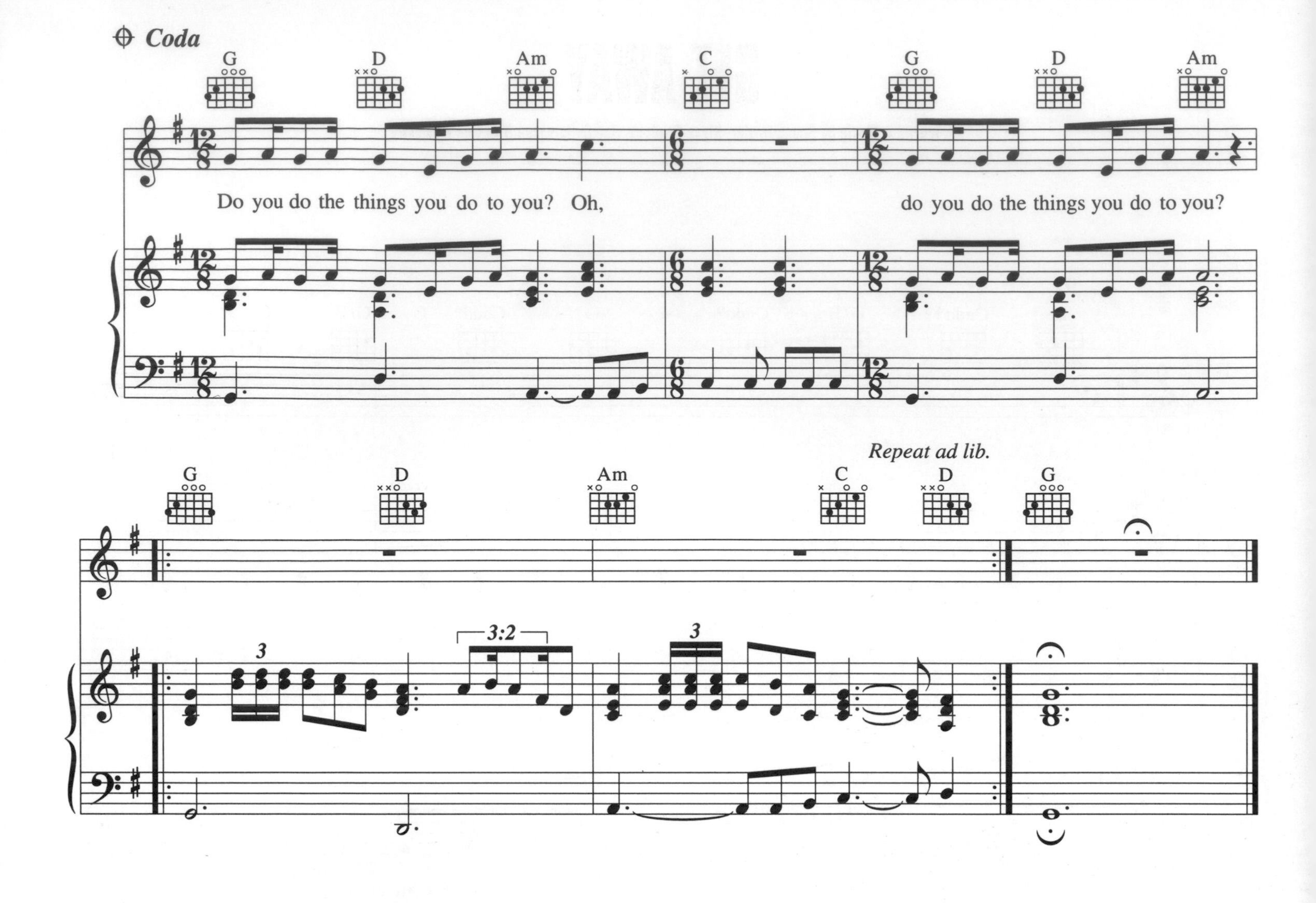

Verse 2:
If I were a king and you were a lady,
What would I sing to say what I'm saying?
And would you believe the verses left open,
My heart on my sleeve, the rhyming all broken?

And how does it feel when the world comes back so real and true?
And how do you do the things you do to you?

Verse 3:
Sell me a river and I'll skate away
To the downstream where I did play.
So easy minded like a hill on the skyline,
Tripped up and blinded, getting lost on the sidelines.

And how does it feel when each word comes back so real and true?
And how do you do the things you do to you?

GET AWAY

Words & Music by Simon Fowler, Steve Cradock, Oscar Harrison & Damon Minchella.

© Copyright 1995 Island Music Limited, 47 British Grove, London W4.
All Rights Reserved. International Copyright Secured.

D
Cadd9
G/B
Cadd9
some of them like to tell a sto - ry that is long and old and
D
Cadd9
G/B
Cadd9
couch it in in - dif - ference and the wine that they were sold to get a -
D
Cadd9
G/B
Cadd9
way, a - way, a - way, a - way, a - way, to get a -
1.
D
Cadd9
G/B
Cadd9
way, a - way, a - way, a - way, a - way. 2. Well

2, 3.
To Coda
G/B
Cadd9
D
Cadd9
Just get a - way, a - way, a - way, a - way, a - way,
G/B
Cadd9
D
Cadd9
G/B
Cadd9
just get a - way.
Well I
D
Cadd9
G/B
Cadd9
used to think my free - dom was a lot of things I'd give, de -
D
Cadd9
G/B
Cadd9
mand - ing on my time but I had so much time to give.
And I

D
Cadd9
G/B
Cadd9
used to think that ev - 'ry - thing was a knee in what you are. But
find - ing out the truth that hurts, so I nev - er went that far, know - ing I'd al - ways get a -
way.
I get a -
way, a - way, a - way, a - way, a - way, a - way a - way, a - way.

Verse 2:
Well someone's got to tell them
That it's not deserved,
Rehearsed or written down
By playwrights over time
Just picking up on the nerve.
And some of them got a difference
That they reserve for you,
Well I like them all but I don't trust any of them,
Well shouldn't you, just get away…

Verse 3:
Well it comes down to the fact
That I'm now different from the past,
Demanding all my ideals
It's just trying to make them last.
And some of the things that you say,
They're ringing home so true.
I hang my head out of the door
And I follow you, yes I follow you and get away.

Exclusive Distributors:
Music Sales Limited
8/9 Frith Street, London W1V 5TZ, England.
Music Sales Pty Limited
120 Rothschild Avenue, Rosebery, NSW 2018, Australia.

Order No. AM939180
ISBN 0-7119-5971-4

This book © Copyright 1996 by Island Music Limited.
Visit the Internet Music Shop at
http://www.musicsales.co.uk

Unauthorised reproduction of any part of this publication by
any means including photocopying is an infringement of copyright.

Book design by Michael Bell Design.
Music arranged by Roger Day.
Music processed by Paul Ewers Music Design.

Your Guarantee of Quality:
As publishers, we strive to produce every book to the
highest commercial standards.
The music has been freshly engraved and, whilst endeavouring to
retain the original running order of the recorded album, the book has been
carefully designed to minimise awkward page turns and to make
playing from it a real pleasure.
Particular care has been given to specifying acid-free, neutral-sized
paper made from pulps which have not been elemental chlorine bleached.
This pulp is from farmed sustainable forests and was produced
with special regard for the environment.
Throughout, the printing and binding have been planned to ensure a sturdy,
attractive publication which should give years of enjoyment.
If your copy fails to meet our high standards, please inform us and
we will gladly replace it.

Music Sales' complete catalogue describes thousands of titles and
is available in full colour sections by subject, direct from Music Sales Limited.
Please state your areas of interest and send a
cheque/postal order for £1.50 for postage to:
Music Sales Limited, Newmarket Road, Bury St. Edmunds, Suffolk IP33 3YB.

Printed in the United Kingdom by
Halstan & Co, Ltd., Amersham, Bucks.

6/97 (279